THIS IS A CARLTON BOOK

Text and Design copyright © 2000 Carlton Books Limited

This edition published by Carlton Books Limited 2001
20 Mortimer Street, London, W1N 7RD

tm and © 1965 and 1999. THUNDERBIRDS is a trademark of
Carlton International Media Limited and is under licence.
THUNDERBIRDS is a Gerry Anderson Production.
Licensed by Carlton International Media Limited.
© 1999. The CARLTON logotype device is a trademark
of Carlton International Media Limited.

A CIP catalogue for this book is available from the British Library.

ISBN 1 84222 228 7

Text: Jenny Olivier
Art Direction: Diane Spender
Design: Carol Wright
Production: Garry Lewis

Lady Penelope's *Secrets*

The **secret agent** of *chic's* personal tips on **beauty**, *fashion* and **lifestyle**.

CARLTON
BOOKS

Contents

Introduction

*H*ello, Lady Penelope here. Welcome to my book of secrets.

You know, for as long as I can remember, people have been saying to me, 'Lady Penelope, what is your secret?' Of course, they didn't realize that as a special agent for International Rescue, secrecy is my trade. But they weren't trying to find out about my latest adventure taking on the evil Hood, or saving the world from destruction. No, what they want to know is the secret of my style. That's why I've decided to write this book.

As an 'It girl' I mixed with the fashionable set and was often asked to model the latest looks on the catwalks of Milan or in the pages of *Vogue*. My life may be quite different today, but I still like to look my best, whether I'm launching a new ship or tracking down a spy. In fact, my work demands almost as many costume changes as I used to make as a model! My International Rescue colleagues may be able to slip into their fetching uniforms every time they set out on a rescue, but as an undercover agent, I need to have the perfect outfit ready for wherever my assignment takes me.

'Perhaps that is **one** of the reasons I *love* my **job**. I may not be on the **catwalks**, but I'm still dressing up.'

Of course, style runs through the Creighton-Ward family like blue blood. The first Lord Creighton-Ward was a courtier during the reign of Elizabeth I, whose elegant doublet and hose and beautiful curls attracted the attentions of many of the ladies of court, including the virgin queen herself. Hundreds of years later, my namesake, Lady Penelope Creighton-Ward, or the Gazelle as she was known in the popular press, was an icon of the 'swinging sixties', famous for her daring Mary Quant mini skirts and dramatic diametric bob, styled exclusively for her by Vidal Sassoon.

But style isn't just a question of designer clothes and chic hairstyles, and doesn't have to be inherited. Style is about elegance, confidence and panache. Style is about the way you look and the way you act, it's reflected in your home and in your work and in the company you keep. It's a way of life.

Inside this book are the secrets of my style. I hope it give you a glimpse of the real Lady Penelope.

Lady Penelope Creighton-Ward

The first Lord Creighton-Ward, the founder of our dynasty and a man who knew just where looking good could get you.

Part 1: The *Look*

The Power of *Pink*

I may be a special agent for the world's number one rescue organization, regularly playing a key role in dramatic assignments and risking my life to save the world from destruction, but many people know me best as the Pink Lady.

Indeed, there is even a Pink Lady cocktail named in my honour and whenever I am in London, I take a trip to my favourite bar, The Match, and drink one of these delicious concoctions of champagne and raspberry liquer.

Pink is my colour. It's the colour of my car, and the colour of many of my favourite outfits.

New York designer Bebe Brighton designed this daring pink and red 'clown' outfit, which I keep for entertaining at my Australian sheep ranch, Bonga Bonga. The evening always seems to go with a swing when I'm wearing it.

This coral-pink shot-silk jacket is one of my favourites. When I wore it on the Anderbad Express monorail I never imagined I'd end up in front of the train, rather than inside it! Thank goodness Virgil and Gordon arrived just in time to save me, and my beautiful jacket.

To me, pink represents the many sides of Lady Penelope. Pink can be gentle and feminine and when I want to look my most alluring, I'll wear an outfit in the softest pink. What man wouldn't stop to help a woman dressed in baby pink? If you think you might need assistance or information from a man, young or old, it's the colour to wear. After all, some-times we girls have to make the most of our feminine wiles to get what we want, at work or at play.

At other times, pink can be playful and fun and I often wear it when entertaining friends at home. Dress in a fun pink outfit and your guests will know to cast formalities aside and have a fab time.

Pink can be *passionate* and powerful. No one who has seen my pink Rolls-Royce, FAB 1, racing down the motorway to another rescue would doubt the power of the *engine* beneath its bonnet (or the guns behind its radiator).

But just because pink works for me, that doesn't make it the right choice for everyone. Pink suits my pale skin, blonde hair and blue eyes, but if you're a dark-skinned beauty, it might not be your colour at all. Take my good friend Tin-Tin. Her ravishing brunette locks and olive complexion suit a very different palette.

A hot pink trouser suit is perfect for a working girl. It's comfortable and chic, and will always stand out in the crowd!

The important thing to do is discover your 'signature' colour and make it your own. Whether you're a pink lady or a scarlet woman, once you've found the colour for you, you'll be amazed at the fun you can have!

When Tin-Tin comes to London, we always make time for a proper girl's day out. I like to take her to the coolest boutiques, to show her what's in and what's out. Last time she visited me, she bought this gorgeous suit in this season's hottest colour, tangerine. I'm sure it caught the eyes of all the Tracy boys when she got home! After a day's shopping, we usually head to the bar in Harvey Nick's for a cocktail. Shopping can be such exhausting work!

Welcome to my
Wardrobe

As a secret agent, I never know when the next assignment is going to come, and where it will take me, from the wilds of the deep south in America to the glamorous French Riviera. When I get the call on my secret transmitter, there's not a moment to lose. I certainly don't have time to worry about what to pack, or which blouse to wear with which skirt. That's why it's so important for me to keep my wardrobe packed with a variety of outfits to suit every occasion.

Even if your job isn't quite so unpredictable, a modern girl needs a wardrobe that's prepared for every eventuality. Pull together a collection of classic pieces, drop in one or two more daring outfits for fun, and you know you'll always look the part.

To show you just what I mean, I've selected some of my favourite pieces. Each offers me a different look but I like to think that each one has that special Lady Penelope pizzazz.

So let me open the doors to my wardrobe, and show you some of the secrets that lie within.

Working *Girl*

When I'm working I want a to show that I mean business, without looking dull and drab. Well-cut suits and simple but classic dresses are the order of the day. As every working girl knows, if you want to be taken seriously, you've got to look the part. So match your male colleague's Armani suits with your own designer labels, and show them you're more than just a pretty face.

When top designer Francois Lemaire called me to ask if I would model for him,
I wanted to meet him in an outfit that was chic and classy. This white dress with
black trim, from Lemaire's winter collection, is simple but devastatingly effective,
and I knew that he would love to see me in it.

Dare to be *Different*

I love to experiment with different fabrics and bold designs. These dresses combine simple cuts with striking effects. Cool enough for the daytime but hot enough for the evening too, if you're wearing a dress like these, you won't have a worry, wherever the night takes you.

A simple design, but the daring use of PVC makes this dress stand out from the crowd. But be careful, it's the kind of dress that can get you into trouble!

A Leopard can Change her *Spots*

The modern girl's wardrobe is full of extraordinary man-made fabrics. I adore the practicality of Francois Lemaire's Penylon. With its amazing shrinking qualities it means I can pack so much more into a suitcase. And when I get to my destination, I know that my dresses will spring to life without a crease or a crumple. I feel confident, and my wonderful chauffeur and valet, Parker, knows he won't be called on to perform miracles with his travel iron!

But sometimes I like to look back on the traditional fabrics of the past. If you want to bring out your sensual side, nothing beats the luxury of fur, snakeskin or leather. And with the miracles of modern technology, these effects can be recreated so convincingly, they'd fool the animals themselves. So you can enjoy the warmth of your mink coat, and know that the minks are still enjoying theirs!

My fake crocodile handbag, in pink of course, seems to have this reptile fooled!

This beautifully tailored snakeskin suit fits me like a second skin!

Shimmering in *Style*

Tin-Tin and I enjoy a girl's night out watching the gorgeous and
talented boy band the Cass Carnaby Five while on assignment
at the Paradise Peaks Hotel. Work and pleasure combined!
I was certainly glad to have packed this glittering dress
and pink jacket with tinsel trim.

This beautiful orange silk dress was designed specially for me by top couturier Ernesto Georgioni and includes pearl and diamante belt and shoulder details created by Tiffany. International Rescue's own designer Brains added the finishing touch, a secret transmitter hidden amongst the diamonds!

An evening *out* on the **town** is the perfect excuse for **glamour** and sometimes a girl needs to pull out all the **stops** in a truly *gorgeous* evening gown.

I adore dresses that shimmer and sparkle. Whether you're enjoying an intimate candlelit dinner with a gentleman friend, or twirling under the flashing lights of the dance floor, with these outfits, you're sure to catch the eye.

I needed something pretty spectacular to match Alan's striped tails, but I think this creation did the trick!

USE YOUR *Head*

Buying beautiful dresses – or if you're really lucky
having them made for you – is one thing, but it's those
little finishing touches that separate the truly stylish
from the fashion victim.

*This perky cap picks up the the bold red and white
of my dress. Combined with long leather gloves
and a matching handbag, it creates the ideal
look for a visit to an art gallery. In fact, you
could say that it was a work of art in itself!*

Hot *Hats*

A natty hat will lift your look to new levels
of style, if you can carry it off with panache. But
finding that perfect hat to match not just the colour of your
outfit but also its style can be tricky. Can I let
you in to one of my own style secrets?
You can make life so much easier by
having hats made to match your
favourite outfits. I'm sure you'll
agree that the price is worth it
when you see the results.

White fur keeps me warm
on the peaks, but can be
just as effective as a piece
of pure fashion.

31

Even practical hats can be stylish: a leopard-skin sash gives extra bite to the hat I wear to protect me from the harsh sun of the Australian outback when I'm visiting my ranch.

It may be a hard hat, but the soft pink colour and matching scarf adds the feminine touch to the most manly of hats, and separates the girls from the men!

It seems a shame to keep this handsome hat for equine occasions.

This daring orange sunhat is one of my absolute favourites.

Lovely Locks and *Diamonds*

Of course, hats aren't right for every occasion, but we ladies have a gorgeous adornment on our heads already. Whether blonde, brunette or fiery redhead, your hair is a natural asset not to be ignored. Piled high in a classy chignon or adorned with sparkling diamonds, your hair can be your crowning glory.

My favourite stylist, Charles Worthington III, from the famous hairdressing dynasty, created these fab styles for me. Every girl should have a hairdresser like Charlie. Once you've found one, don't let him go (and keep him to yourself)!

A diamond-encrusted tiara will make any girl feel like a princess, even a lady!

Glamorous hair adornments are all the rage on the international fashion scene at the moment, and I have been making the most of the famous Creighton-Ward family jewels.

Mixing **antique jewels** with up-to-the-minute fashions *creates* an effect that's truly **flawless.**

But beware, if you are wearing the real thing it might be wise to avoid a trip to the casino. As my dear friend the Duchess of Royston discovered, when the chips are down, you might just lose your sparkle!

Right: They say diamonds are a girl's best friend, and this sparkling pink pearl and diamond hair clip has certainly been a friend to me. Not only does it look divine, it's also useful for picking locks! With the help of my butler, Parker, an expert in that particular field, it's got me out of a few jams.

Ribbons *Bows & Bands*

Sometimes diamonds and pearls can seem a little over the top, but that doesn't mean your hair has to go unadorned. Ribbons, bows and decorative bands can all add a playful edge to the chicest look and show that, though you may have a high-powered career, you're still a girl at heart!

My favourite hairband, in pink, of course. It was created for me by Estella Jagger, the heir to the Jagger fortune and an old schoolfriend of mine.

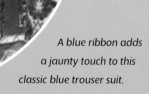

A blue ribbon adds a jaunty touch to this classic blue trouser suit.

Look in the mirror and you'll spot my subtle black bow.

Going *Undercover*

Sometimes International Rescue calls on me to go on an undercover investigation. Unfortunately, as a member of the 'in crowd', I can't avoid the attentions of the press. The gossip columns love to discuss my latest look, or my latest admirer, and to reveal where I've been and who I was with. However much I try to avoid it, the paparazzi always seem to catch me, whether I'm attending a movie premier or going to my favourite restaurant with a good friend. Sometimes I wish I had one of International Rescue's special camera detectors in my handbag.

Captured by the paparazzi once again!

So going undercover requires more than a false name and a convincing cover story, I also need a whole new look. When I was sent to investigate that gorgeous boy band, the Cass Carnaby Five, I took on the role of professional singer Wanda Lamour. To give myself a new look, I donned a jet black wig, turning myself from blonde to dark-haired beauty.

As a final effect, I added a beauty spot on my left cheek and showed off my raven looks to their best with a white hairband.

Even if you're not planning a complete **change** of **identity**, a *new* look could be just what the doctor ordered, whether it's for that *special* night out or something **more** permanent.

*Every girl likes the chance to try
something new, and what better
excuse than a fancy dress party.*

*At the Monte Bianco fancy dress ball.
I think Parker enjoyed dressing up
as much as I did. And doesn't he
look dashing in canary yellow?*

A girl could lose her head in this Marie Antoinette wig!

Thank goodness there's plenty of headroom in FAB 1.

Beauty *Secrets*

I love the glamorous side to my work, travelling to exciting locations, meeting extraordinary people and having the most thrilling adventures. My job truly is a dream come true.

But sometimes, things can get a little messy, like the time I was sent to find the impostors who were posing as International Rescue, and bringing our good name into disrepute. One of our American agents, a rather strange little man called Jeremiah, had tracked the impostors down to a cave near his home in the deep South. I rushed to the scene, but found myself in a rather sticky situation when I fell face-first into the oozing mud.

Once I had cleaned myself up, I found that the mud had given my skin a glowing freshness, just like a mudbath in the most exclusive health spa. But that's not the way I'd choose to keep the glow in my cheeks and the sparkle in my eyes!

Like most girls, my make-up bag is an essential item and I never travel without my lipstick and powder. For me, it's not just a matter of looking my best, it could save my life. My compact holds a secret more important than any formula to hide wrinkles or blemishes – a transmitter. When I look into the mirror Jeff Tracy can see and hear me, wherever I am. Jeff and I have even worked out a special code so that I can send messages to him using only my powder puff and lipstick. To the eyes of anyone watching me, I'm simply reapplying my make-up. Little do they know that I'm calling International Rescue!

My dressing table onboard FAB 2 holds my favourite make-up items, including a bottle of Soupçon de Peril.

Mind you, I always make sure the powder in my special compact comes from my favourite beauty range, Les Secrets des Femmes, and that my lipstick is the perfect shade to match my outfit. That way I can mix beauty with business.

There's nothing like flying down the slopes to bring a healthy glow to your cheeks. You could say Tin-Tin and I were cheating a bit with our jet packs, but with a gunman after us, we were in danger of something worse than piling on the pounds!

Before I go out in the evening, I make time for a moment in front of the mirror to apply lipstick, powder and rouge. And I never go out without a splash of Soupçon de Peril, my own exclusive scent, created for me by the famous perfumer, Jacques Verre. But I believe that a truly beautiful complexion doesn't come out of a bottle or a jar.

My *beauty* secrets are as old as the hills. Nothing beats eating well and getting plenty of regular **exercise**. And keeping *fit* doesn't just make you **look good**, it could get you out of all sorts of dangers!

At the end of the day, there's one way to ensure that you'll look bright and beautiful in the morning – an early night. When I've finished another demanding assignment, I head for bed to catch up on my beauty sleep. And I always sleep soundly, knowing that International Rescue is out there.

Part 2: The *Style*

Playing it *Cool*

Style isn't just about the way you look. It's also about the way you act. And the most important rule to remember is: Play it Cool.

As a special agent, I need to keep my nerves at all times. My work can get me into some pretty nasty scrapes, too. I've been at the wrong end of a pointed gun more times that I'd care to mention. On one occasion, I was kidnapped at gunpoint from my yacht, FAB 2. I was investigating the theft of the plans for a nuclear device. In the wrong hands the plans could have caused the destruction of the world. My only hope of finding the thieves was to lure them out of hiding, using myself as bait.

It wasn't long before they'd fallen into my trap. A gunman appeared on FAB 2 and took me to a deserted boathouse. It looked as though I'd gone from hunter to prey, but I kept my cool. First I found out what the gunman intended to do. You

Passing on the necessary information wasn't easy but I managed to keep my cool, thanks to my compact.

can always rely on the villainous classes to boast about their plans to their victim. It makes them feel powerful, but actually makes them weak. With a little cajoling he explained that he intended to blow the boathouse sky high. Not only would the explosion get rid of me, it would also cause a distraction at just the right time, giving him and his gang the chance to escape from the bay in their submarine.

I had found out what I needed to know about the thieves' whereabouts, but how could I pass this information on to International Rescue, and save myself and the stolen plans? By using my feminine wiles, of course. I asked the gunman if I could at least fix my make-up before he tied me up. He fell for it, calling me a crazy dame. Little did he know that my compact was also a transmitter with a direct link to Tracy Island. International Rescue came through, saving me and the stolen plans. Thank goodness for my cool nerves and my compact. Sometimes a girl's make-up bag really is her best friend!

Of course, keeping your cool isn't always easy and just occasionally even I lose my nerve. Like the time I went on my first rescue mission. I had been longing to be part of an actual rescue ever since I joined International Rescue, in fact, the boys had been teasing me about it that very day. Unfortunately they would soon have more to tease me about.

When a call came through, Jeff allowed me to join Virgil in Thunderbird 2. I felt so excited to be part of the team. When we arrived in the danger zone I stayed in Thunderbird 2. This was a job for the boys. But I wasn't alone in the ship. As I sat waiting for Virgil to return, I suddenly saw the one thing guaranteed to make me lose my cool – a mouse! To this day, Virgil has never let me forget how my nerves of steel turned to jelly at the sight of that tiny harmless little fellow.

Well, even the coolest customers sometimes loses their nerve. But don't forget, stay calm, cool and collected, because if you ever find yourself in real danger, you know that International Rescue won't be far away.

A Helping *Hand*

Like most modern girls, I find it hard to juggle all the demands of my busy life. My job takes me around the world, and into some pretty hot spots, but I also have a home to run, and not any old home, but a huge stately manor, Creighton-Ward Mansion. Then there's my ranch in Australia, Bonga, Bonga, the yacht FAB 2, the ocean-going cruiser, Seabird, my car, FAB 1 and my beautiful racehorse, FAB 3.

On top of that I receive so many invitations to parties and premieres, night clubs and fashion shows all over the world

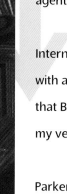

that sometimes I don't know whether I'm in London, Paris or New York. Well, even a secret agent has to let down her hair sometimes.

International Rescue helps make my life easier with all the high-tech labour-saving gadgets that Brains invents for me, but I also have my very own secret weapon: Parker.

Parker is my butler, but he's so much more than that. Chauffeur, bodyguard,

and companion, he's as adept with a gun or a set of safe-cracking tools as he is with a silver tray or a crystal decanter, and in my line of business, that comes in handy.

Parker comes from a long line of butlers, but he wasn't an old family retainer, and I didn't engage him from one of the reputable agencies. No, he came to me by a very different route.

You see, with all the gadgets of the modern home, the demand for butlers has declined drastically. Despite his impeccable training, Parker found it hard to get work and fell in with the notorious villains of the London underworld. Known to his friends as Nosey, Parker gained a reputation as the world's finest safe-cracker and cat burglar, a reputation that landed him in Parkmoor Scrubs prison.

Parker's safe-cracking skills came in handy when we had to break into the vault of the Bank of England to save a workaholic accountant trapped inside. Even the latest high-tech wizardry, created to make the bank's vaults the safest in the world, was no match for Parker, aided only by one of my hair pins!

After his release, Parker attempted to make an honest living (at least, that's what he's always told me) but his past associates tracked him down and soon he was back to his old ways, which is where I came in. I don't like to associate with the criminal classes, but in my business it's useful to have a finger on the pulse. My contacts in the underworld keep me in touch with who's who and what's what. You never know when the information might come in handy. (And they do make fascinating company!) I'd heard of Parker though my sources, and thought his prodigious talents might be put to better use, on the right side of the law.

With the help of a friend, a wealthy oil tycoon, I laid a trap and caught Parker red-handed: helping himself to the contents of my friend's safe. I made him an offer he couldn't refuse: come to work for me, or return to Parkmoor!

*Parker at the wheel of FAB 1.
I may be in the backseat, but
I'm always in control!*

Since then, Parker has been indispensable to me. Whether he's firing the guns of FAB 1 or serving drinks at Creighton-Ward Mansion, I can always rely on him. Well, almost always.

Unfortunately, Parker picked up a few bad habits during his years in the criminal world and sometimes the temptations are too much. I always make sure I keep his safe-cracking tools well hidden in case he decides to brush up his skills!

Parker's links with the criminal fraternity can come in handy, but every so often his loyalties waver. Like the time his old

cell mate, Light Fingered Fred, escaped from Parkmoor. When he heard there was trouble at the Bank of England, Parker assumed it was Fred up to his old tricks, and tried to stop me reaching the scene in order to protect him. Of course, in the end he was no match for Lady Penelope!

But when it comes to the crunch, I know that I can trust Parker with my life. And he does make a splendid cup of tea.

Arriving in *Style*

I may be International Rescue's London agent, but that doesn't mean that all my assignments are close to home. My work has taken me to the cafés of Paris and the casinos of Monte Carlo, an Alpine hotel and even America's deep south.

Wherever I go I love to dip my toes into the culture and customs of the place. When in Rome, as they say! In Paris, my favourite drink is Pernod, at least it was until I nearly fell victim to a poisoned Pernod! Thank goodness Parker was keeping a sharp eye on things. Since then, I've stuck to that other famous French tipple – champagne – and I always try to find a bottle of my favourite vintage, 1993, a very good year.

In Monte Carlo I adore to visit the casinos, though I have to keep an eye on Parker. Last time we were there he gambled away FAB 2, my beautiful yacht. It took a while to sort out that little mess!

At the casino with Parker.

Off on holiday. I'm afraid Parker's taste in summer clothes leaves something to be desired!

Sometimes I need to get away from it all, so Parker and I slip into something casual and take off for a beach resort.

We recently took a trip to Monte Bianco, a fashionable resort on the Mediterranean. Its hip hotels and golden beaches have made it this season's hottest spot for the fashionable set. But it got a little too hot when we were there. Who

would have thought that we'd travel all that way for some peace and quiet, only to find ourselves, and the resort, in terrible danger and in need of the help of International Rescue?

Monte Bianco hotel, an exclusive hangout where the rich and famous go to get away from the pressures of celebrity.

Parker and I agree, first class really is the only way to travel. Though after my last adventure, I won't be taking the Anderbad Express monorail again!

FAB 1

But of course if you really want to travel in style, the most
reliable way to do it is in the comfort of your own car. That is,
at least, if you have a car like FAB 1.

FAB 1 was created exclusively for my father, Hugh
Creighton-Ward, by the Rolls-Royce Corporation. Built for
speed and comfort, she guarantees a smooth ride, even in

Parker had plenty of experience of speeding away from the scene of the crime in his past life. Now he uses the same driving skills to take us in the opposite direction.

the most difficult situations. With her plush leather interior and climate-controlled cabin, FAB 1 keeps me as cool as a cucumber as I rush to the danger zone. And with a speed of up to 200 m.p.h., I know I'll never miss out on the action!

I don't believe in travelling light. After all, I need to know I'll have the perfect outfit for any eventuality, wherever I go. With FAB 1's ample boot and large cabin, there's plenty of storage space, though somehow I always manage to fill it!

I was a young girl when FAB 1 was commissioned, but I had already developed my taste for pink and dear daddy had her painted in my favourite shade. When I inherited her, I made a few modifications of my own, to make FAB 1 a thoroughly modern madam. (Well, every lady needs the occasional makeover!) There's the hydrofoils for travel on water, skis for use on snow and studs in the tyres for icy roads. Now I can take FAB 1 just about anywhere, or rather, she can take me!

Inside, FAB 1 is packed with the latest technology, including a computer monitor and video communications console so I can keep in touch with International Rescue, watch a  movie, or log in to the Internet to pass the time on a long journey. Just occasionally, though, reception can be a little difficult to maintain.

There's also the small matter of the armoury. Front and rear machine guns, canon, harpoon launchers, smoke-screen canister, oil slick dispenser and laser guns are just some of the secret weapons hidden inside FAB 1. A girl has to protect herself, especially in my line of business.

Sleek and smooth, but packing a punch beneath her cool exterior, I like to think that FAB 1 is a little like her owner.

FAB

The Creighton-Wards have always had a nautical bent, and I adore life on the ocean waves, especially in the luxury of my ocean-going yacht, FAB 2.

As you know, I always like to have the right look, and when I'm aboard FAB 2, I slip into this nautical little number.

*Relaxing on the poop
deck of FAB 2.*

The family has a fleet of ships of all
shapes and sizes moored around the
world from the Caribbean to the Indian
Ocean, but when I joined International Rescue,
I decided I needed a boat that would combine the
Creighton-Ward style with technological gadgetry that
would impress even Brains. Jeff Tracy recommended
International Engineering to me, and they certainly
fulfilled all my requirements when they created FAB 2.

The latest nautical and communications technology keeps
me in contact with Tracy Island wherever I sail, and I'm
well protected with my torpedoes and titanium alloy hull.
But what I really love about FAB 2 is the
luxurious interior which makes every
journey a pleasure cruise.

I keep FAB 2 moored in an exclusive
private marina on the south coast of
England, but just like me, she's always
prepared to haul up the anchor and set
off on another exciting adventure as
soon as the call comes through.

An English Woman's
Home

If you really want to know a girl's secrets, perhaps the best place to start looking is her home. As far as I'm concerned, the jetset lifestyle has its charms but, as the saying goes, there's no place like home. And that's certainly true of my home, Creighton-Ward Mansion.

Creighton-Ward Mansion is built on the site of a Norman castle and has been a place of courtly pleasures and intrigue since those long ago days. The first Lord Creighton-Ward selected the beautiful rolling hills of Foxelyheath for his home after he was knighted by Elizabeth I. The queen herself was a regular visitor to the house he built, enjoying the fine hunting on the 2,000-acre estate that remains in Creighton-Ward hands to this day.

This carving of the family crest was one of the few pieces to survive the fire in 1729 and now sits atop the fireplace of the library, my favourite room for receiving guests.

The current Creighton-Ward mansion was built in 1730 by the famous dandy, Lord Cuthbert Creighton-Ward. Lord Cuthbert, an amateur scientist, had burned the original family home to the ground while experimenting with a new

form of gunpowder. He asked architect Colen Campbell to design this imposing Palladian edifice, a fitting replacement.

Since then, each successive generation has added their own unique touches to the house, while keeping true to its spirit. I am no exception. Take my bedroom. The four-poster bed, armchairs and marble table all date back to the eighteenth century and could seem a little austere for a young lady. But by adding pink curtains to the bed, a few pink cushions and a bedspread covered in pink roses, I've stamped my own feminine mark on the room. The beautiful roses, picked fresh from the garden every morning by Parker, are the finishing touch.

Most of my additions, however, are more difficult to detect. As far as the eye can see, Creighton-Ward mansion seems to have changed very little for hundreds of years and people often tell me that walking into the house is like stepping back in time. With its rich brocade and marble, antique furniture and priceless artefacts, it resonates with a grandeur and nobility of times gone by.

The grand staircase is decorated with statues of Lord Cuthbert Creighton-Ward's own wife, Lady Emelia, a legendary beauty. They lead to the doors of the library which are flanked by marble busts of two of my illustrious ancestors.

Who would think that behind the august stones and rich decoration of this stately pile, the most sophisticated technology is buzzing and whirring? I've added a satellite antenna and a number of two-way video communication consoles for contacting International Rescue, and a sophisticated computer in the east wing controls many of the household functions, including heating, power supply, security and communications. It makes life so much easier for the staff and my house guests know that they can rely on all the mod cons of a modern home.

Creighton-Ward Mansion is my sanctuary, a place of peace and tranquillity, and nowhere could be more peaceful than the beautiful bower I had built in the west garden. It's here that I go to think and read. But, of course, with the help of a transmitter in my silver tea pot, International Rescue can reach me even in this secluded spot.

Watching a movie in the drawing room with my good friend Brains. I like to keep things informal when entertaining close friends.

It would be a shame to keep Creighton-Ward Mansion to myself, however, as it really is the perfect place for a party and I do love to entertain.

I believe in making my guests feel at home, whether it's a few close friends or a large house party. I always plan the menu with care – in discussion with my wonderful cook Lil, an absolute darling who trained at the illustrious Jamie Oliver School of Fine Food – and make sure there's plenty of entertainment available, from the latest holographic movies to a horseback ride around the estate.

Below: *Christmas at Creighton-Ward Mansion.*

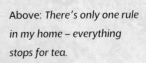

Above: *There's only one rule in my home – everything stops for tea.*

Bonga *Bonga*

Though Creighton-Ward Mansion is my primary residence,
I have inherited a number of properties around the world.
My family always believed that travel broadened the mind.

Of all our properties, my favourite is the Australian ranch,
Bonga Bonga, which was acquired by Bertie 'Buster'
Creighton-Ward, who moved to Australia when things got
a little 'hot' for him in London. I love the wide open spaces
of the Australian outback and I often come to the ranch
to relax, and to check up on my sheep. You can never be
too careful with those sheep rustlers about!

Jeff Tracy and Parker relax in the lounge at Bonga Bonga and make use of the state-of-the-art entertainment system I installed.

This circular concrete fireplace couldn't be more different from the highly decorated marble fireplace in the library of Creighton-Ward Mansion, but each goes perfectly with its setting.

When I inherited Bonga Bonga it was in dire need of repair, and I had it totally redecorated in a modern style. The open-plan lounge with its modern fabrics and simple geometric designs makes quite a change from the rich detailing of Creighton-Ward Mansion. But, as with my clothes, I love to experiment with different styles and fabrics when it comes to interiors. Once again it's all about getting the right thing for every occasion, or, in this case, every location!

Part 3: **The Real** *Lady Penelope*

The Men in My *Life*

I'm not the kind of girl to spill the beans on my latest admirer, but they do say you can know a man by the company he keeps, and the same is true for a woman. So let me introduce you to my favourite company, the Tracy family.

Jeff Tracy

Jeff Tracy is the founder of International Rescue, and a dear, dear friend of mine. The son of a Kansas wheat farmer (his mother, an absolute angel, lives with him today), he had a distinguished career in the US Airforce before moving to the Space Agency. Jeff was one of the dashing astronauts who captured the hearts of young girls around the world when they landed on the Moon during those days when it was still uncolonized.

Ex-pilot and astronaut Jeff Tracy gets a rare chance to show off his flying skills.

Tragedy struck when Jeff's beautiful wife died, leaving him with five young sons to bring up single-handedly. Fortunately, Jeff isn't the kind of man to crumple in the face of adversity. Turning to the commercial world, he was soon making his way in civil and construction engineering. Before long he was one of the richest men in the world. But money isn't what drives Jeff and when he read about a terrible air crash in which eighty people died due to inadequate rescue equipment, he found his mission. Within two years, International Rescue was established.

It was around this time that Jeff came into my life. I was working as the chief operative of the Federal Agents Bureau (quite an achievement at my young age, I don't mind telling you) and was fascinated by the stories I was hearing about a mysterious organization that was performing miraculous rescues around the world. I had set my own investigation underway to discover their secrets when International Rescue came to me! It seems that Jeff had also heard of me, and wanted me to come on board. Who could resist such an offer of adventure?

Since then, Jeff has become so much more than a boss to me. Though I'm closer in age to his sons, I like to think Jeff listens to me, and values

Jeff and I share tastes in many things, and we both love a gripping adventure story. You'd think we had enough adventures in real life!

Jeff at Bonga Bonga, obeying my strict instructions to relax. I think he could do with a bit of Lady Penelope magic on his wardrobe too!

my advice. Once I even managed to convince him to take a holiday with me at Bonga Bonga, not an easy job to do with a man so dedicated to his work. Not surprisingly, it wasn't long before he was back at Tracy Island, and in command.

Charming and entertaining, with a million **extraordinary** stories to tell, *Jeff Tracy* is a **gentleman** to the core.

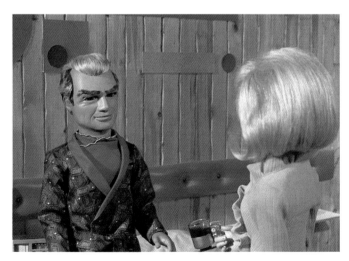

Like all Americans I know, Jeff can't start the day without a strong cup of coffee.

Scott *Tracy*

Jeff's eldest son, Scott, has inherited his father's love of adventure, not to mention his dashing good looks.

The pilot of Thunderbird 1, Scott is always first on the scene of any rescue and that's the way he likes it! Fast-talking and quick-thinking, Scott has the confidence to make quick decisions and stick by them, and he's never lost for words, which makes him a fascinating companion. When I'm with Scott, I know the quick-witted banter is sure to flow.

Scott was educated at Yale and Oxford, and I like to think that our special brand of British charm rubbed off on him during his time in Blighty. I remember attending a ball at Oxford while he was there, and wondering who the handsome and self-

Thunderbird 1's handsome pilot.

What girl wouldn't want to be rescued by the dashing Scott Tracy.

assured American student could be. Little did I know that one day I would be working alongside him!

As the eldest son, Scott knows that one day the running of International Rescue may fall to him, and when Jeff is absent, Scott takes command. It's a heavy weight for such young shoulders, but I know he's up to the job.

I hope that one day **Scott** will find the right girl. She'll need to be a *spirited lady* to keep up with him, but what a **catch!**

Scott is a natural leader, and is often in command of the rescues, but that's not to say that he's arrogant. He'll muck in with the rest of the team and occasionally even takes a spell of duty in Thunderbird 5. In fact, he's the kind of older brother that any boy, or girl, would love to have.

Virgil *Tracy*

While Scott is the spit of a young Jeff Tracy, Virgil has inherited the refined good looks of his mother, and many of her qualities too.

Grandma Tracy tells me that Mrs Tracy was a beautiful and sensitive creature, who gave up a promising career as a concert pianist to look after her husband and young boys, whom she adored. Like her, Virgil has a thoughtful and creative nature, and he is a fine pianist. I always make time to talk to Virgil about what's happening on the music scene, and I know I can rely on his recommendations for new sounds.

Virgil is also something of an artist, and loves to visit Creighton-Ward Mansion to admire the many works of art that my family has collected over the years.

Sensitive he may be, but like all the Tracy brothers, Virgil is also fearless and brave. As the pilot of Thunderbird 2 he has an

important role in almost every rescue, and his courage and ingenuity is never in doubt. He truly is a renaissance man.

Intelligent, *loyal*, and a man of **honour**, Virgil will make a **wonderful** husband to the lucky **lady** who catches his *heart*.

Alan *Tracy*

Ah, Alan, the joker of the pack. This boy is guaranteed to bring a smile to your face, even when you find you're the victim of one of his pranks.

Before the creation of International Rescue, Alan Tracy was a big name on the Formula One circuit, famous not only for his dare-devil driving but also for his blonde locks and baby-faced good looks. He built up quite a following among female fans, I can tell you.

These days he gets his kicks speeding into outer space in Thunderbird 3 and shows just as much courage on rescue operations as he ever did on the race track.

A night out on the town with Alan.

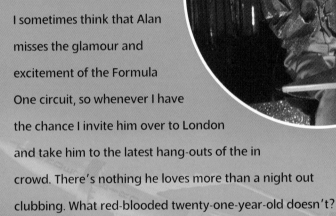

I sometimes think that Alan misses the glamour and excitement of the Formula One circuit, so whenever I have the chance I invite him over to London and take him to the latest hang-outs of the in crowd. There's nothing he loves more than a night out clubbing. What red-blooded twenty-one-year-old doesn't?

But there's one thing that is certain to stop Alan from straying too far from Tracy Island – Tin-Tin Kyrano. Of course, they like to think that we don't know it, but you'd have to be blind not to see the spark between these two young lovers.

And though Alan's **head** might occasionally be turned by a London beauty, his **heart** is always **true** to his *real love* back home.

Gordon *Tracy*

All the Tracy brothers are at their physical peak, they need to be for their work, but Gordon is the real athlete of the family. This one-time Olympic swimmer excels at all sports, but the water is his true element. In fact, he spends much of his time in the sea, whether it's manning Thunderbird 4 or scuba diving off the rocky coast of Tracy Island.

Gordon's used to getting in to deep water. As the pilot of Thunderbird 4, it's his job!

Gordon is the first to share one of Alan's jokes. Sometimes they're as thick as thieves and you know they're up to something. His lively nature makes him a great guy to be about, but the high spirits mask a deeper side, a permanent scar, perhaps, from his close shave with death in a high-speed hydrofoil crash.

Still, you can always **rely** on Gordon to be the life and *soul* of any party. And if the going gets **hot**, he'll be there to *save* you.

John ⬤ *Tracy*

John is the quietest of the Tracy boys, and not just because he spends much of his time far out in space running Thunderbird 5.

John is a true intellectual, a man more of thought than of deed. Slighter in build than his brothers, he is tremendously lithe and has the extraordinary grace and poise for which his mother is remembered. His passion is astronomy and he has written numerous books on the subject. He even discovered a new quasar system, now called the Tracy system in honour of the family.

Ever on the alert, John passes another emergency message to Tracy Island.

John loves the contemplative life that Thunderbird 5 affords him, though just occasionally he does long to play a part in the action-packed adventures of his siblings. But, of course, as the one who monitors emergency calls from around the world, no one could be more important to the running of International Rescue than John.

A man of *mystery* with hidden depths, John is a real **hard nut** to crack, even with my many skills at getting beneath the surface! But he's well worth the effort. When you get to know him, he truly is a *fascinating* man.

Brains

I couldn't finish this chapter without mentioning the other man in the team, Brains. He may not have the Tracy brothers' dashing looks or confidence, but as every woman knows, a truly clever man holds many attractions.

Orphaned at the age of twelve when a hurricane struck his Michigan home, Brains was adopted by a Professor of Cambridge University who recognized a child prodigy in the making. When Jeff Tracy realized he needed a brilliant scientist to help him accomplish his plans for International Rescue, his search led straight to Brains. He couldn't have made a better choice.

The creator of all the Thunderbirds craft and the many gadgets that we use in our rescues, Brains combines scientific genius with an amazing

Deep in thought, who knows what amazing invention Brains is planning?

Brains to the rescue!

creative flair for imagining the impossible, then making it
happen. His ingenious gizmos have got me out of trouble
on more than one occasion.

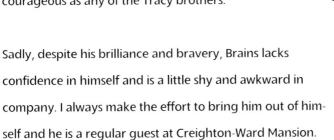

Brains is very much the backroom boy, but every
now and then he finds himself at the centre of
the action, and when he does, this man of
science shows his true mettle. When the
occasion demands it he can be as bold and
courageous as any of the Tracy brothers.

Sadly, despite his brilliance and bravery, Brains lacks
confidence in himself and is a little shy and awkward in
company. I always make the effort to bring him out of himself and he is a regular guest at Creighton-Ward Mansion.

Perhaps his anxious *stutter* is the result of the
tragedy of his childhood, but Brains has found
a *true family* in International Rescue.

The Private Lady *P*

Well, there you have it. I've given you a guided tour of my home, my wardrobe, my friends and my lifestyle. I hope you found pleasure and inspiration in these pages.

But what about the private Lady Penelope, what lies beneath the cool exterior? What are her hopes and dreams, her fears and fantasies?

Let me reveal one more style secret before I go: a woman of mystery will never lose her fascination!

So, who is the real Lady Penelope? That's one secret I'm keeping to myself.

Lady Penelope Creighton-Ward